# Away We Go!

## 100 Poems for the Very Young

Compiled by CATHERINE SCHAEFER McEWEN

Illustrated by BARBARA COONEY

New York: Thomas Y. Crowell Company

LIBRARY OF CONGRESS CATALOG CARD NO. 56-7798

Seventh Printing

Grateful acknowledgment is made to the following publishers and authors for special permission to reprint copyrighted material:

Abelard-Schuman, Inc., for selections from *Up the Windy Hill* by Aileen Fisher: "If I Had a Cardboard Box," "Horses," "The Picnic Box," "The Green Silk Bug," "Do Rabbits Have Christmas?" "After a Bath," and "Little Brother," copyright 1953 by Aileen Fisher.

Artists and Writers Guild, Inc., for "Things of Summer," and "Brown Bear's Honey Song," from *The New Golden Almanac* by Kathryn Jackson, copyright 1952 by Simon and Schuster, Inc., and Artists and Writers Guild, Inc.

Child Training Association, Inc., publishers of *Children's Activities* magazine, and the authors, for the following poems: "A New Friend," by Marjorie Allen Anderson (by permission of Laurel A. Stevick); "Home Grown," by Helen Houston Boileau; "Ready for Winter," by Clarice Foster Booth; "Home Again," by Enola Chamberlin; "The Merry-Go-Round," by Electa Clark; "Hallowe'en Scare," by Charlotte Yoder Cutler; "Away We Go!" by Eleanor Dennis; "Traffic Light" and "Our Milkman," by Nona Keen Duffy; "Late Winter on Our Beach," by Burnham Eaton; "Walking," by Grace Glaubitz; "The Sun," by Louise Fabrice Handcock; "A Hurry-up Word" and "Quiet Please," by Emily M. Hilsabeck; "A Jolly Noise," by Ethel Jacobson; "Spring Song," "Signs of Christmas," and "Lickety-Lick," by May Justus; "Snowflakes" and "Sleepy Song," by Marian Kennedy; "Day Song," by Eleanor Hammond (by permission of Eleanor Doar); "Surprise," by Billee Eckert Martin; "Change of Seasons," by James Steel Smith; "Mother's Day," by Aileen Fisher.

Albert C. Clarke, for "September," from *The Children's Year* by Margaret Wise Brown, published by Harper & Brothers.

Marchette Chute, for "My Dog," from *Rhymes About Ourselves,* published by The Macmillan Company.

Katherine H. Dent, for "When You Send a Valentine," by Mildred J. Hill.

Doubleday & Company, Inc., The Society of Authors, Miss Rose Fyleman, and *Punch:* for "Singing Time," from *The Fairy Green* by Rose Fyleman, copyright 1923 by Doubleday & Company, Inc.

E. P. Dutton & Co., Inc., for "Bridges" and "Under the Ground," from *Stories to Begin On* by Rhoda Bacmeister, copyright 1940 by E. P. Dutton & Co., Inc.

Field Enterprises, Inc., for "That Duck" and "The Earthworm," from *Childcraft* (1948 edition), copyright by Field Enterprises, Inc.

Aileen Fisher and *Story Parade,* for "Early, Early Easter Day," by Aileen Fisher.

Friendship Press, Inc., for "Birthday Presents" (arranged from the Japanese), from *The Whole World Singing,* compiled by Edith Lovell Thomas. Copyright, Friendship Press, Inc.

Harper & Brothers: for "Autumn Woods" and "Let's Pretend," from *A World to Know* by James S. Tippett, copyright 1933 by Harper & Brothers; for "Park Play," from *I Live in a City* by James S. Tippett, copyright 1927 by Harper & Brothers, copyright 1955 by James S. Tippett; and for "A-Caroling on Christmas Eve," from *Counting the Days* by James S. Tippett, copyright 1940 by Harper & Brothers.

Houghton Mifflin Company, for "The Bird's Nest," from *All About Me* by John Drinkwater.

Parents' Institute, Inc., publishers of *Humpty Dumpty's Magazine* and the authors of the following poems: "Slow Pokes," by Laura Arlon; "Strange Footprints," by Vivian Gouled; "The Frog on the Log," by Ilo Orleans; "Happy New Year," by Mildred Evans Roberts; "April Weather" and "Maytime Magic," by Mabel Watts.

*Jack and Jill* and Ivy Eastwick, for "Mary's Lullaby," copyright 1947 by The Curtis Publishing Company.

J. B. Lippincott Company: for "E is the Escalator," from *All Around the Town* by Phyllis McGinley, copyright 1948 by

TO  NANA  AND  PAL

# Contents

### Me and Mine

### The Outside World

## Nature and the Seasons

## Living Creatures

## Special Days

## Poems for Fun

## Widening Horizons

# I: Me and Mine

## Singing-Time

I wake in the morning early
And always, the very first thing,
I poke out my head and I sit up in bed
And I sing and I sing and I sing.

ROSE FYLEMAN

3

# Park Play

Every morning
I can play
In the park
Across the way.

I can run
And I can shout.
I am glad
When I come out.

JAMES S. TIPPETT

4

# Ready for Winter

I have a fur cap
  And mittens, just new.
My coat is so heavy
  No cold can get through.

With stout leather boots
  And stockings, wool-red,
I shall keep nice and warm
  From my toes to my head.

My nose? Never fear!
  I've a scarf round about
That leaves only space
  For my eyes to peep out.

CLARICE  FOSTER  BOOTH

## Snowy Morning

Every where
   I walk
      And go,

I leave
   My
      Step-marks
        In
           The
              Snow.

BARBARA  YOUNG

## Thaw

The snow is soft, and how it squashes!
"Galumph, galumph!" go my galoshes.

EUNICE  TIETJENS

# If I Had a Cardboard Box

Has anyone a shoe box?
Or any box at all?
I can make houses out of boxes
if they are not too small.

I can put chimneys on them,
and cut out window squares,
and put a smaller box on top
to make a nice upstairs.

The doors have cardboard hinges,
the porch stays up with blocks . . .
why, I could make a CASTLE
if I had a cardboard box.

AILEEN FISHER

# Sleepy Song

Mother sings a sleepy-song,
   Hushaby—oh!
A lovely little sleepy-song,
   Soft and low.

A song of little kittens
   And fleecy, white sheep;
Of puppies and of bunnies
   Going to sleep;

A song of little baby birds
   Asleep in a tree.
A lovely little sleepy-song,
   Just for me.

MARIAN KENNEDY

# My Teddy Bear

I have a little teddy bear,
Who goes to bed with me.
Although he cannot say a word,
I like his company.

BETTE  OLGIN
*(age 6)*

# II: The Outside World

## Moon-Come-Out

Moon-Come-Out
And Sun-Go-In,
Here's a soft blanket
To cuddle your chin.

Moon-Go-In
And Sun-Come-Out,
Throw off the blanket
And bustle about.

ELEANOR FARJEON

12

# Day Song

At nighttime, when I go to bed,
A million stars shine overhead.
But when I wake up in the day,
There's just one sun to light my play.

ELEANOR HAMMOND

# A New Friend

They've taken in the furniture;
I watched them carefully.
I wondered, "Will there be a child
Just right to play with me?"

So I peeked through the garden fence
(I couldn't wait to see).
I found the little boy next door
Was peeking back at me.

MARJORIE ALLEN ANDERSON

13

# Away We Go!

Hippity-hop!
Skippity-skop!
We've hopped so long
Our feet won't stop.

We say hello
To those we meet
And hippity-hop
On down the street!

ELEANOR DENNIS

# Sliding

Down the slide
We ride, we ride.
Round we run, and then
Up we pop
To reach the top,
Down we come again.

MARCHETTE CHUTE

# Portrait

Always in a hurry,
    Always on the go—
That's my little sister.
    Don't I know!

MARCHETTE CHUTE

# A Hurry-Up Word

Skedaddle!
I don't think I ever heard
Such a hurrying-kind of word!
I like it, too; it has a sound
That in my mind goes round
    and round
And makes my feet skip off the
    ground!
Skedaddle!
    Skedaddle!
        Skedad-dad-daddle!

EMILY M. HILSABECK

15

# *Walking*

When Daddy
Walks
With Jean and me,
We have a
Lot of fun
'Cause we can't
Walk as fast
As he,
Unless we
Skip and
Run!
I stretch,
And stretch
My legs so far,
I nearly slip
And fall—
But how
Does Daddy
Take such steps?
He doesn't stretch
At all!

GRACE GLAUBITZ

## The Picnic

We brought a rug for sitting on,
Our lunch was in a box.
The sand was warm. We didn't wear
Hats or Shoes or Socks.

Waves came curling up the beach.
We waded. It was fun.
Our sandwiches were different kinds.
I dropped my jelly one.

DOROTHY ALDIS

# Quiet Please

"Sh-h-h! Sh-h-h!"
Mother whispers.
"Baby is sleeping!
So pretend you're a mouse
When you come through the house
And, like a mouse,
Come creeping! Come creeping!
Sh-h-h!
    Sh-h-h!
        Sh-h-h!"

EMILY M. HILSABECK

# Our Milkman

"Anything extra
  Today, today?"
I hear our friendly
  Milkman say.

Our kitchen clock
  Shows half-past eight.
Right on time!
  He's never late!

He sets three quarts
  Outside our door
Unless we leave
  A note for more.

NONA  KEEN  DUFFY

19

# A Jolly Noise

Gurgle, gurgle, gurgle, gurgle,
Glug, glug, glug—
Goes the milk from the bottle
When I pour it in my mug.

Gurgle, gurgle, gurgle, gurgle,
Glug, glug, glug—
Goes the water down the drain
When I pull the bathtub plug.
Gurgle,
gurgle,
gurgle,
gurgle,
glug!

ETHEL   JACOBSON

20

# *Like Me*

A garbage man is a garbage man
Who rattles and bangs the garbage can.

Like me.

A policeman carries a club in his hand.

Like me.

The mailman carries a bag. Like mine.
And they all of them always have a good time.

Like me.

DOROTHY  ALDIS

21

# E *Is the Escalator*

*E* is the Escalator
  That gives an elegant ride.
You step on the stair
With an easy air
  And up and up you glide.
It's nicer than scaling ladders
  Or scrambling 'round a hill,
For you climb and climb
But all the time
  You're really standing still.

PHYLLIS  MC GINLEY

# *Drinking Fountain*

When I climb up
   To get a drink,
It doesn't work
   The way you'd think.

I turn it up.
   The water goes
And hits me right
   Upon the nose.

I turn it down
   To make it small
And don't get any
   Drink at all.

MARCHETTE CHUTE

# The Merry-Go-Round

Oh, the merry-go-round,
  The merry-go-round,
    I love to ride on the merry-go-round!

The music is loud,
  The music is gay.
    Hear the noisy calliope play!

Up and down,
  Wild and fast,
    The horses go galloping, galloping past!

Oh, the merry-go, merry-go
  Round-and-round!
    I love to ride on the merry-go-round!

ELECTA CLARK

# *Traffic Light*

We're waiting, and we're waiting,
  And we're looking overhead;
For the signal light is orange.
  Now we see that it is red!

We're watching, and we're watching,
  And we're paticnt in between
While we're waiting for the changing
  Of the light from red to green.

We're waiting, and we're staying
  In the place right where we are;
But now the green is showing,
  And my mother starts the car!

NONA  KEEN  DUFFY

# The Airplane

The airplane taxies down the field
And heads into the breeze,
It lifts its wheels above the ground,
It skims above the trees,
It rises high and higher
Away up toward the sun,
It's just a speck against the sky
    —And now it's gone!

AUTHOR UNKNOWN

# Bridges

I like to look for bridges
Everywhere I go,
Where the cars go over
With water down below.

Standing by the railings
I watch the water slide
Smoothly under to the dark,
And out the other side.

RHODA BACMEISTER

27

# Lickety-Lick

Lickety, lickety, lickety-lick!
The frosting is getting thickety-thick—
The beautiful frosting
That Mother will take
To trim up the wonderful
Company cake!
But some of the sweet stuff
Is certain to stick
To the bowl and the spoon.
Judy, Johnny, come quick;
Here's the bowl,
Here's the spoon
For a lickety-lick!

MAY JUSTUS

28

## Hunger and Thirst

It's nice to be hungry,
It's nice to be fed
With a thick brown slice
Of Mother's bread.

And a drink of milk,
A long cool drink,
Is one of the nicest things,
I think.

BARBARA YOUNG

29

# Lying Awake

I like to lie awake at night
And watch the shining of the light
Along the city street.
I like to hear the stepping sounds
Of all the people's feet.

I wonder where
They're going to,
And what they say,
And what they do,
And how their faces look,
And who
Is waiting home
For them—
I like—to lie—
Awake—
Ho-hum!

BARBARA  YOUNG

# III: Nature and the Seasons

# Late Winter on Our Beach

Late in March in the high-wind sky
The wild geese honk and the sea gulls cry.

The great sun beats on the cracked packed ice,
And the droplets drip in a twinkling trice.

Low on the rocks where the icicles run,
The terns and the teeter-bobs bask in the sun.

They own our beach with its cold, gold sand
And perch on the empty ice-cream stand.

                                    BURNHAM  EATON

# Change of Seasons

Earlier, earlier
  Comes the sun;
    Later and later
      The day's done;
        Shorter and shorter,
        Dark of night;
          Longer and longer,
          The warm light.

JAMES STEEL SMITH

# The Winter Is Past

For, lo, the winter is past,
The rain is over and gone;
The flowers appear on the earth;
The time of the singing of birds is come,
And the voice of the turtle is heard in our land.

*from* THE SONG OF SONGS

33

# Surprise

Last week I played
Out in the park,
Coasting on my sled.
Today I looked
For snow and found
A violet instead!

BILLEE ECKERT MARTIN

# Spring Song

I know, I know, I know it—
    The spring is here at last!
There's dogwood on the hillside;
    The redbud's coming fast;
Wake-robin's in the wildwood;
    There's wild geranium.
I know, I know, I know it—
    The lovely spring has come!

MAY JUSTUS

35

# Spring-Signs

Everywhere the wind blows
There goes spring—
Red kites and green kites
Are tugging at the string.

Walks have hardly dried
Until marbles roll about
Long before the colored flowers
In the fields are out.

Maybe frost has lingered,
And a touch of snow—
But there are little spring-signs
Where the children go.

MILDRED BOWERS ARMSTRONG

# April Weather

An April day . . . an April day,
So full of many things,
A primrose, and a puppy,
And a bird with bright blue wings.

An April day . . . an April day,
And everything's just right,
A little shower, a little sun,
. . . A breeze to sail my kite!

MABEL WATTS

# Kite Days

A kite, a sky, and a good firm breeze,
And acres of ground away from trees,
And one hundred yards of clean, strong
    string—
O boy, O boy! I call that Spring!

MARK SAWYER

# Home Grown

I carefully spade up the ground
    And rake it very neatly.
I plant the tiny seeds in rows,
    Then cover them completely.
The rains come down, the sun shines out,
    The warm spring breezes blow.
Then in a week, or maybe two,
    My plants will start to grow.

I watch my garden every day.
    At last I see some shoots.
They let me know that down below
    My little plants have roots.
Because I sowed a lot of seeds,
    Before long I'll be able
To pick some carrots, beans, and peas
    And flowers for our table.

HELEN HOUSTON BOILEAU

# Spring

The leaves are uncurling,
   My seedlings are up.
The sunlight is warmer,
   We've got a new pup.
The robins are building,
   I've painted my bike,
And we can go barefoot
   Whenever
      we
        like.

MARCHETTE CHUTE

39

# Summer Morning

Summer morning
  Bright and early,
Winds are waking,
  Clouds are curly.
Honey-bees are hovering,
  Birds are stirring,
Voice and wing.
  Everything
Is rosy, pearly,
  Summer morning
    Bright and early.

BARBARA YOUNG

40

# In the Summer

In the summer, in the evenings,
When the day's been very warm,
Then we walk without our shoes on
In the long grass on the farm.

And the fireflies in the bushes
Prick the darkness all around,
And the crickets, very busy,
Make their night time summer sound.

And the grass is cold and dewy
After all the long day's heat,
But the stepping stones set in it
Still are warm beneath our feet.

DOROTHY ALDIS

# Water Noises

When I am playing by myself,
And all the boys are lost around,
Then I can hear the water go;
It makes a little talking sound.

Along the rocks below the tree,
I see it ripple up and wink;
And I can hear it saying on,
"And do you think? And do you think?"

A bug shoots by that snaps and ticks,
And a bird flies up beside the tree
To go into the sky to sing.
I hear it say, "Killdee, killdee!"

Or else a yellow cow comes down
To splash a while and have a drink.
But when she goes I still can hear
The water say, "And do you think?"

ELIZABETH MADOX ROBERTS

# *Shore*

Play on the seashore
And gather up shells,
Kneel in the damp sands
Digging wells.

Run on the rocks
Where the seaweed slips,
Watch the waves
And the beautiful ships.

Find dead crabs
And ivory bones,
Slices of pearl
And moony stones.

Take off your stockings
And wet your feet,
Wading in the water
Where pools are deep.

MARY BRITTON MILLER

# *Things of Summer*

Summer's full of smelling things—
   Mint and mignonette,
And clove pinks and new hay,
   And earth that's warm and wet.

Summer's full of things to hear—
   Sound of birds and bees,
And small feet that scurry,
   And rustlings in the trees.

Summer's full of things to touch—
   Grass and leaves and logs,
Shells and sand and water,
   And slippery fish and frogs.

But some things of summer
   Are only for the eyes—
The bloom of scarlet poppies,
   The wings of butterflies.

KATHRYN JACKSON

# The Sun

There's sun on the clover
And sun on the log,
Sun on the fish pond
And sun on the frog,

Sun on the honeybee,
Sun on the crows,
Sun on the wash line
To dry the clean clothes.

LOUISE FABRICE HANDCOCK

## In August

When the sun is strong
   And the day is hot,
We move around
   At a peaceful trot.
We don't wear much
   In the way of clothes
And we squirt ourselves
   With the garden hose.

MARCHETTE CHUTE

46

# September

Apples heavy and red
Bend the branches down,
Grapes are purple
And nuts are brown,
The apples smell sharp and sweet on the
    ground
Where the yellow bees go buzzing around.
And way up high
The birds fly southward
Down the sky.

MARGARET WISE BROWN

# Autumn Woods

I like the woods
    In autumn
When the dry leaves hide the ground,
When the trees are bare
And the wind sweeps by
With a lonesome rushing sound.

I can rustle the leaves
    In autumn
And I can make a bed
In the thick dry leaves
That have fallen
From the bare trees
Overhead.

JAMES S. TIPPETT

48

# Snowflakes

Whirling, swirling, rushing, twirling,
   Sifting through the air—
Snowflakes scurrying, scampering, hurrying,
   Falling everywhere.

Gently sliding, floating, gliding—
   Making not a sound;
Lightly dancing, skipping, prancing,
   Fluttering to the ground.

Whirling, swirling, rushing, twirling
   'Gainst the windowpane—
Snowflakes scurrying, scampering, hurrying.
   Winter's here again!

MARIAN KENNEDY

# White Fields

## I

In the winter time we go
Walking in the fields of snow;

Where there is no grass at all;
Where the top of every wall,

Every fence, and every tree,
Is as white as white can be.

## II

Pointing out the way we came,
—Every one of them the same—

All across the fields there be
Prints in silver filigree;

And our mothers always know,
By the footprints in the snow,

Where it is the children go.

JAMES  STEPHENS

# IV: Living Creatures

# My Dog

His nose is short and scrubby;
  His ears hang rather low;
And he always brings the stick back.
  No matter how far you throw.

He gets spanked rather often
  For things he shouldn't do,
Like lying-on-beds, and barking,
  And eating up shoes when they're new.

He always wants to be going
  Where he isn't supposed to go.
He tracks up the house when it's snowing—
  Oh, puppy, I love you so!

MARCHETTE CHUTE

# *Horses*

Back and forth
and up and down,
horses' tails go switching.

Up and down
and back and forth,
horses' skins go twitching.

Horses do
a lot of work
to keep themselves from itching.

AILEEN FISHER

53

# Baby Goat

Did you ever pat a baby goat
And learn how soft he feels?
Did you ever watch him walk about
On his four little black high heels?

ZHENYA GAY

# Ways of Traveling

Little Mister Polliwog,
You swim to and fro.
When you turn into a frog
You'll hop where'er you go.

ALICE WILKINS

54

# The Frog on the Log

There once was a green
  Little frog, frog, frog,
Who played in the wood
  On a log, log, log!

A screech owl sitting
  In a tree, tree, tree,
Came after the frog
  With a scree, scree, scree!

When the frog heard the owl
  In a flash, flash, flash,
He leaped in the pond
  With a splash, splash, splash!

**ILO ORLEANS**

## Slow Pokes

Turtles are slow,
As we all know,
But
To them
It is no worry,
For
Wherever they roam,
They are always at home,
So
They do not
HAVE
To hurry.

LAURA   ARLON

# A Rainy Day

The chickens run inside the coop
   As fast as they can get
As soon as it begins to rain,
   They do not like the wet.

The horses droop their heads and tails
   And sulk about the rain.
The cows all gather in the barn
   And won't go out again.

The kittens sit with ruffled fur.
   The turkeys make a fuss.
But all the ducks are full of joy
   And come to play with us.

MARCHETTE CHUTE

# The Earthworm

Earthworm, earthworm,
   Crawling all around,
Teaching all your babies
   How to loosen up the ground,
Going up and down,
Going up and down.

When I met you,
   Little earthworm,
Crawling through the ground,
   You looked so very funny
   That I laughed to see you
Wiggle round and round,
Wiggle round and round.

GROUP POEM
*(by children)*

# Under the Ground

What is under the grass,
Way down in the ground,
Where everything is cool and wet
With darkness all around?

Little pink worms live there;
Ants and brown bugs creep
Softly round the stones and rocks
Where roots are pushing deep.

Do they hear us walking
On the grass above their heads;
Hear us running over
While they snuggle in their beds?

RHODA BACMEISTER

# The Picnic Box

When we get out the car,
and are dressed for town,
our dog gives a yawn
and lies right down.

When we get out the car
and the Picnic Box,
our dog gives a bark
you can hear for blocks.

Our dog gives a bark
you can hear for MILES,
and his tail makes curves
that are shaped like smiles.

AILEEN FISHER

# The Green Silk Bug

We found a beautiful Green Silk Bug
that was crawling over the playhouse rug,
and we put our beautiful Green Silk Bug
in a sandpile hole we hurried and dug.

And we built him a house on a sandy street
and put in some lettuce for him to eat
and a piece of rubber to wipe his feet
and a leather button to make a seat.

And then we said to the Green Silk Bug
who looked quite at home in the hole we dug:
"If you could talk, you'd probably say,
'MY, I was lucky to come this way.'"

AILEEN FISHER

# *The Bird's Nest*

I know a place, in the ivy on a tree,
Where a bird's nest is, and the eggs are three,
And the bird is brown, and the eggs are blue,
And the twigs are old, but the moss is new,
And I go quite near, though I think I should
    have heard
The sound of me watching, if I had been a
    bird.

JOHN DRINKWATER

# V: *Special Days*

# *Happy New Year*

Hang the new calendar
High on the wall.
See winter and spring days,
And summer and fall,
Play days and work days,
And warm days and colder.
One day's my birthday
Then I shall be older!

MILDRED EVANS ROBERTS

# When You Send a Valentine

When you send a valentine—
That's the time for fun!
Push it underneath the door,
Ring the bell and run, run, run!
Ring the bell and run!

MILDRED J. HILL

# Early, Early Easter Day

Easter Day we got up early.
Morning still was gray and pearly,
Chimney smoke was not yet curly,
Early, early Easter Day.

Out into the dawn we hurried,
Up the hill we skipped and scurried.
Would we see it? We were worried.
Would we see it, Easter Day?

We looked east, and just that minute
Something round, with fire within it,
Started rising, while a linnet
Sang a song for Easter Day.

First the sun was red and flaring,
Then it turned all golden-glaring,
As we stood there staring, staring,
Early, early Easter Day.

AILEEN  FISHER

# Dandelions

I'm picking my mother a present.
    How perfectly glad she will be
To see all the beautiful flowers
    She gets on her birthday from me.

MARCHETTE CHUTE

67

# Mother's Day

It isn't just on Mother's Day
That Mother likes a special smile,
Although we honor her in May,
It isn't just on Mother's Day
She likes the special things we say—
She likes them all the while!
It isn't just on Mother's Day
That Mother likes a special smile.

AILEEN FISHER

# Fourth of July Night

Just see those pin wheels whirling round
Spitting sparkles on the ground,
And watch that rocket whoosh so high,
Then turn to flowers in the sky—
Green and yellow, blue and red.
And look at ME still not in bed!

DOROTHY ALDIS

# Hallowe'en Scare

On Hallowe'en my friends and I
   Dress up in frightening clothes.
We each put on a funny face
   With an e-nor-mous nose.

We ring our neighbors' doorbells,
   And they get an awful fright
To see such scary creatures
   Standing there at night!

CHARLOTTE YODER CUTLER

70

# The Pilgrims Came

The Pilgrims came across the sea,
And never thought of you and me;
And yet it's very strange the way
We think of them Thanksgiving Day.

We tell their story old and true
Of how they sailed across the blue,
And found a new land to be free
And built their homes quite near the sea.

Every child knows well the tale
Of how they bravely turned the sail,
And journeyed many a day and night
To worship God as they thought right.

The people think that they were sad,
And grave; I'm sure that they were glad—
They made Thanksgiving Day—that's fun—
We thank the Pilgrims every one!

ANNETTE WYNNE

# Signs of Christmas

Dancing, prancing
Here and there
Round a corner,
Up a stair,
Through a doorway,
Down a street—
Hurry, scurry
Go the feet.
Hustling, bustling
In and out,
Folks go gaily
All about.
From the signs
We see and hear,
Christmas time
Is very near!

MAY JUSTUS

# A-Caroling on Christmas Eve

On Christmas Eve
We always meet
For singing carols
On our street.

We sing the carols—
Three or four—
In front of every
Neighbor's door.

And through the opened doors
We see
Each neighbor's
Lighted Christmas tree.

JAMES S. TIPPETT

# Round and Round

Twist the tinsel,
  Flashing bright,
Round the tree
  For our delight.
Twining, shining,
  Overhead,
Wind the lights of
  Green and red.
Now join hands, and
  So will we
Circle round the
  Christmas tree,
Singing still the
  Holy word
That the watching
  Shepherds heard:
"Peace on earth,
  Good will to men"—
Jesus' birthday
  Comes again!

DOROTHY BROWN THOMPSON

74

# Birthday Presents

Cup of warm milk, Baby Jesus,
    Present from the Cow;
She has given it for your birthday.
    Drink it, drink it now!

Woolly blanket, Baby Jesus,
    Present from the Sheep;
It will be a soft, white cover
    When you go to sleep.

If you're hungry, Baby Jesus,
    What will you eat then?
Taste this brown egg, you will like it,
    Brought by Mother Hen.

EDITH LOVELL THOMAS
*(Arranged from the Japanese)*

# Long, Long Ago

Winds thro' the olive trees
   Softly did blow,
Round little Bethlehem
   Long, long ago.

Sheep on the hillside lay
   Whiter than snow;
Shepherds were watching them,
   Long, long ago.

Then from the happy sky,
   Angels bent low,
Singing their songs of joy,
   Long, long ago.

For in a manger bed,
   Cradled we know,
Christ came to Bethlehem,
   Long, long ago.

AUTHOR UNKNOWN

# Mary's Lullaby

Little Dove,
   Little Darling,
Little Sparrow,
   Little  Starling,
Little Light,
   Little Joy,
Little Treasure,
   Little Boy.

IVY O. EASTWICK

# Cradle Hymn

Away in a manger,
No crib for a bed,
The little Lord Jesus
Lay down his sweet head;
The stars in the heavens
Looked down where he lay,
The little Lord Jesus
Asleep in the hay.

The cattle are lowing,
The poor baby wakes,
But little Lord Jesus
No crying he makes.
I love thee, Lord Jesus,
Look down from the sky,
And stay by my cradle
Till morning is nigh.

MARTIN LUTHER

# VI: Poems for Fun

# Let's Pretend

Let's pretend we're elephants
  Who trample down tall grass
Who force their way through jungles
  And trumpet as they pass.

JAMES S. TIPPETT

# No Drip of Rain

It rained on Anne,
it rained on Fan,
it rained on Arabella,
but—
it did not rain
on Mary Jane—
SHE had a HUGE umbrella.

IVY O. EASTWICK

# Spring Rain

The storm came up so very quick
    It couldn't have been quicker.
I should have brought my hat along,
    I should have brought my slicker.

My hair is wet, my feet are wet,
    I couldn't be much wetter.
I fell into a river once
    But this is even better.

MARCHETTE CHUTE

81

# Do Rabbits Have Christmas?

Do rabbits have Christmas,
I wonder, I wonder?

They have little spruces
to celebrate under,
where snow has made pompons
with silvery handles,
and frost has made tinsel
and icicle candles.

Do rabbits have presents,
I wonder, I wonder?

They have little fir trees
to celebrate under.
But do they have secrets
and smiles on their faces?
Let's go put some carrots
in rabbit-y places!

AILEEN FISHER

82

# Blum

Dog means dog. And cat means cat.
And there are lots of words like that.

A cart's a cart to pull or push.
A leaf's a leaf on tree or bush.

But there's another word I say
When I am left alone to play.

The word is Blum. Blum is a word
That very few have ever heard.

It is very nice to hum.
Or you can shout it: BLUM BLUM BLUM.

But shout or whisper, hum or sing,
It doesn't mean a single thing.

DOROTHY ALDIS

# Crescent Moon

And Dick said, "Look what I have found!"
And when we saw we danced around,
And made our feet just tip the ground.

We skipped our toes and sang, "Oh-lo.
Oh-who, oh-who, oh what do you know!
Oh-who, oh-hi, oh-loo, kee-lo!"

We clapped our hands and sang, "Oh-ee!"
It made us jump and laugh to see
The little new moon above the tree.

ELIZABETH MADOX ROBERTS

# Brown Bear's Honey Song

Apple blossom honey is crystal white
(But I don't care a tittle, I don't care a mite),
Buckwheat honey's 'most as dark as me
(But I don't care a bittle, I don't care a bee),
Gooseberry honey is a pale, pale green
(But I don't care a button, I don't care a
    bean),
Golden is the honey from the goldenrod
(But I don't care a smidgeon, I don't care a
    pod),
Honey is honey, and honey is sweet—
And never mind the color when it's time to eat!

KATHRYN JACKSON

# Strange Footprints

It seemed that a giant
   Tramped through the snow,
Or maybe an elephant—
   No one could know.

Everyone guessed
   Whose the footprints could be,
But no one imagined
   Galoshes and me!

VIVIAN GOULED

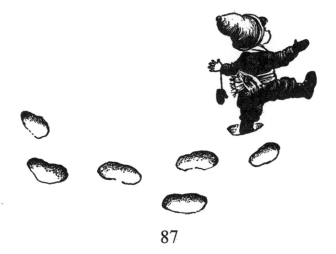

# *After a Bath*

After my bath
I try, try, try
to wipe myself
till I'm dry, dry, dry.

Hands to wipe
and fingers and toes
and two wet legs
and a shiny nose.

Just think how much
less time I'd take
if I were a dog
and could shake, shake, shake.

AILEEN   FISHER

# VII: Widening Horizons

# Maytime Magic

A little seed
For me to sow . . .

A little earth
To make it grow . . .
A little hole,
A little pat . . .
A little wish,
And that is that.

A little sun,
A little shower . . .
A little while,
And then—a flower!

MABEL  WATTS

# Little Brother

"Look, there's a robin.
There goes another.
See all the robins,"
said Ruth's little brother.

I saw a blackbird.
Ruth saw a wren
But her brother said, "Look!
There's a robin again."

I saw a bluebird.
Ruth saw a lark.
But her brother saw ROBINS
all over the park.

Then I said to Ruth,
and Ruth said to me,
"EVERYthing's robins
when you're still just three."

AILEEN FISHER

# Mumps

I had a feeling in my neck,
And on the sides were two big bumps;
I couldn't swallow anything
At all because I had the mumps.

And Mother tied it with a piece,
And then she tied up Will and John,
And no one else but Dick was left
That didn't have a mump rag on.

He teased at us and laughed at us,
And said, whenever he went by,
"It's vinegar and lemon drops
And pickles!" just to make us cry.

But Tuesday Dick was very sad
And cried because his neck was sore,
And not a one said sour things
To anybody any more.

ELIZABETH MADOX ROBERTS

# Playgrounds

In summer I am very glad
    We children are so small,
For we can see a thousand things
    That men can't see at all.

They don't know much about the moss
    And all the stones they pass;
They never lie and play among
    The forests in the grass.

They walk about a long way off;
    And, when we're at the sea,
Let father stoop as best he can,
    He can't find things like me.

But when the snow is on the ground
    And all the puddles freeze,
I wish that I were very tall,
    High up above the trees.

LAURENCE ALMA-TADEMA

# Arbor Day

To plant a tree! How small the twig,
And I beside it—very big.
A few years pass; and now the tree
Looks down on very little me.
A few years more—it is so high
Its branches seem to touch the sky.
I did not know that it would be
So vast a thing to plant a tree.

DOROTHY BROWN THOMPSON

94

# Who Has Seen the Wind?

Who has seen the wind?
  Neither I nor you:
But when the leaves hang trembling
  The wind is passing thro'.

Who has seen the wind?
  Neither you nor I:
But when the trees bow down their heads
  The wind is passing by.

CHRISTINA  ROSSETTI

# Snow

The snow fell softly all the night.
It made a blanket soft and white.
It covered houses, flowers, and ground,
But did not make a single sound!

ALICE  WILKINS

# The Twins

The two-ones is the name for it,
And that is what it ought to be,
But when you say it very fast
It makes your lips say *twins,* you see.

When I was just a little thing,
About the year before the last,
I called it two-ones all the time,
But now I always say it fast.

ELIZABETH  MADOX  ROBERTS

# Indian Children

Where we walk to school each day
Indian children used to play—
All about our native land,
Where the shops and houses stand.

And the trees were very tall,
And there were no streets at all,
Not a church and not a steeple—
Only woods and Indian people.

Only wigwams on the ground,
And at night bears prowling round—
What a different place to-day
Where we live and work and play!

ANNETTE WYNNE

# That Duck

How did that duck
   Know how to swim?
It waddled down
   And jumped right in.
But then it has
   A feather coat
That's just as good
   As any boat.

BRITTAN MAC I.
(*Original verse by a child*)

# Elizabeth Cried

Elizabeth cried
Because I came.
I never tried
To play a game,
I ate my meat
And I looked away—
Till Elizabeth's feet
Ran up, to stay.

We played a game
All over the place,
She said my name,
And I washed her face,
I gave her a ride—
Till my time was spent,
And Elizabeth cried
Because I went.

ELEANOR FARJEON

# Home Again

I like to make a visit
　To the mountain or the shore;
To hear the song of pine trees
　And the ocean's high-tide roar.

But the best time of the visit,
　The sweetest time, is when
Vacation days are over
　And we're all back home again.

ENOLA　CHAMBERLIN

# *Nosegay*

Violets, daffodils,
   roses and thorn
were all in the garden
   before you were born.

Daffodils, violets,
   red and white roses
your grandchildren's children
   will hold to their noses.

ELIZABETH  COATSWORTH

# Other Books of Poems

The following list is not intended as a complete bibliography of poetry for young children. It is, rather, merely a guide for parents and other adults working with children so that they may more easily find their way to some of the additional material particularly suited to the very young child.

Aldis, Dorothy, *All Together*. G. P. Putnam's Sons, New York, 1952.

Brewton, John E. and Sara W., *Index to Children's Poetry*. H. W. Wilson Company, New York, 1942.

Brewton, John E. and Sara W., *Index to Children's Poetry*, First Supplement, 1954. H. W. Wilson Company, New York, 1954.

Chute, Marchette, *Rhymes About Myself*. The Macmillan Company, New York, 1932.

Chute, Marchette, *Rhymes About the City*. The Macmillan Company, New York, 1946.

Chute, Marchette, *Rhymes About the Country*. The Macmillan Company, New York, 1941.

*Children's Activities* magazine. Published by the Child Training Association, Inc., Chicago.

Doane, Pelagie, *A Small Child's Book of Verse*. Oxford University Press, New York, 1948.

Fisher, Aileen, *Up the Windy Hill*. Abelard-Schuman, Inc., New York, 1953.

Geismer, Barbara Peck, and Suter, Antoinette Brown, *Very Young Verses*. Houghton Mifflin Company, Boston, 1945.

*Golden Book of Poetry, The*. Simon and Schuster, Inc., New York, 1947.

Jackson, Kathryn, *The New Golden Almanac*. Simon and Schuster, Inc., New York, 1952.

McFarland, Wilma, *For a Child*. Westminster Press, Philadelphia, 1947.

*Romney Gay's Picture Book of Poems*. Grosset and Dunlap, Inc., New York, 1940.

# *Index of Authors*

**105**

# *Index of Titles*

# *Index of First Lines*

**109**